The GAMBOLS

BOOK Nº 39
by Barry Appleby

£2.50

PULL THE CURTAINS GEORGE

I DON'T LIKE **ANY** EYES STARING AT ME WHEN I'M DRESSING

SPRING IS HERE DARLING— JUST LISTEN TO THE DAWN CHORUS

YES.. ER.. I DON'T MIND YOU TEACHING THEM TO FEED OUT OF YOUR HAND MY SWEET...

BUT **PLEASE** WOULD YOU TEACH THEM NOT TO WAKE US EVERY MORNING AT **DAWN**

YOU CAN'T HAVE MISSED THE FACT THAT WE ARE USING
COLOUR IN THIS YEAR'S ANNUAL FOR THE FIRST TIME

COLOUR HAS TAKEN OFF IN A BIG WAY THESE DAYS IN
THE SAME WAY THAT IT HAS TAKEN IN TELEVISION
— THAT IS PROGRESS — BUT INEVITABLY THERE ARE
SOME PEOPLE WHO PREFER THE CARTOONS IN BLACK
AND WHITE JUST AS THEY HAVE BEEN FOR THE
PAST THIRTY EIGHT YEARS

DON'T WORRY — WE HAVE SELECTED PLENTY
OF CARTOONS IN BLACK AND WHITE TO KEEP
EVERYBODY HAPPY — WE HOPE!

IT'S EASY ENOUGH TO REMEMBER WHICH WAY TO TURN THE CLOCK FOR SUMMER TIME IF YOU RECALL THE OLD SAYING "SPRING FORWARD — FALL BACK" — EVEN IF YOU DO HAVE TO USE AN AMERICANISM FOR AUTUMN!

EEK! WE'VE FORGOTTEN TO PUT THE CLOCK BACK!

THE TIME IS EXACTLY...

JUST ONE DAY OF THE YEAR WE GET THE CHANCE TO HAVE AN EXTRA HOUR IN BED...

....AND AN EXTRA HOUR IN BED I'M GOING TO HAVE

GEORGE DEAR— DON'T FORGET TO ALTER THE CLOCKS

AH YES

OF COURSE— I COULD DO IT MYSELF....

BUT I LIKE TO LET HIM KEEP HIS FANTASY THAT HE'S THE HEAD OF THE HOUSEHOLD

THANKS FOR ROLLING UP TO THE HOUSE SO QUIETLY

TIPPY TOES

©1989 Barry Appleby

I DON'T THINK GAYE HEARD ME SLIP AWAY — I'M REALLY LOOKING FORWARD TO A GAME ON OUR OWN...

.... WITHOUT HAVING OUR WIVES CHATTERING ALL THE WAY ROUND

7-5

A RECENT SURVEY SHOWS THAT IT'S UNFASHIONABLE TO WEAR FURS THAT COME FROM ANIMALS

SUPER!

©1990 Barry Appleby

IT'S MUCH SMARTER TO WEAR SIMULATED FUR COATS

WONDERFUL NEWS

BUT I DON'T BELIEVE A WORD OF IT

4-3

SIX O'CLOCK? ON A SUNDAY MORNING?

OF COURSE

©1989 Barry Appleby

I WON'T GET ON THE FIRST TEE FOR HOURS AND HOURS IF I'M LATE

AND THIS IS THE MAN WHO ONLY LAST WEDNESDAY GRUMBLED ABOUT HAVING TO TURN OUT EARLY TO GET TO WORK ON TIME

16-7

GAYE SOON FOUND THAT HAVING A CAR OF HER OWN DOES HAVE CERTAIN DISADVANTAGES!

LATER AT HOME

SORRY DEAR—BUT THERE WASN'T ROOM IN THE CAR FOR YOU

BUT OF COURSE IF I HAD A CAR OF MY VERY OWN....

©1989 Barry Appleby
4625

MONDAY, TUESDAY

DO YOU MIND IF I USE THE CAR TODAY TO CARRY MY SHOPPING?

WEDNESDAY, THURSDAY

I PROMISED TO TAKE OLD MRS GRASSCUTTINGS TO VISIT HER DAUGHTER

I'LL NEED THE CAR TODAY FOR...

FRIDAY

GAYE DARLING—I'VE HAD AN IDEA—HOW WOULD YOU LIKE A CAR OF YOUR OWN?

©1989 Barry Appleby
4626

THERE WAS A TIME WHEN WHEN THE SALES WERE CONFINED TO JANUARY AND THE SUMMER— NOW THEY SEEM TO GO ON ALL THE YEAR ROUND

GAYE FINDS IT DIFFICULT TO UNDERSTAND TEENAGERS
BUT SHE HAS NO DOUBT WHATEVER THAT THEY WILL
GROW UP TO BE FIRST CLASS PEOPLE

GEORGE ALWAYS FORGETS GAYE'S BIRTHDAY—HIS EXCUSE—USED EVERY YEAR AND WEARING A BIT THIN NOW—IS THAT IT'S DIFFICULT TO REMEMBER AS SHE NEVER LOOKS ANY OLDER

THERE'S NOTHING WORSE THAN A TOOTHACHE

ER...ER..UM

DUDDER DUDDER DUDDER

YES~ THAT REMINDS ME TOO....

I'LL MAKE AN APPOINTMENT FOR YOU WITH THE DENTIST TODAY

©1989 Betty Appleby

4646

D·I·Y
DRILLS
ELECTRIC HAMMER

GAS

NO~I'LL WALK ~ I NEED THE EXERCISE

BUS

THE DENTIST..ER.. NO.. HE WAS CLOSED WHEN I GOT THERE

©1989 Betty Appleby

4647

THE BIG EVENT OF OUR YEAR WAS
HAVING A REAL LIVE BABY TO MIND
WHILE HIS MOTHER WAS IN HOSPITAL

HOW MANY WOMEN FEEL THAT IT'S ALL TOO
MUCH—NOT QUITE SURE <u>WHAT</u> PRECISELY—
JUST EVERYTHING—AND THAT TO GO ON STRIKE
IS THE ANSWER FOR BETTER CONDITIONS—
WELL GAYE CARRIED OUT HER THREAT

THE OCCASIONAL VISITS FROM OUR NIECE AND NEPHEW BRIGHTEN OUR LIVES ENORMOUSLY

VISITORS ARE ALWAYS WELCOME—
BUT OH DEAR THEY DO MAKE
A LOT OF EXTRA WORK

GAYE FOUND THE PARROT SURPRISINGLY GOOD COMPANY

THE TROUBLE WITH TELLING THE
HAIRDRESSER THAT YOU LEAVE IT TO HIM
WHEN HE ASKS YOU HOW YOU WOULD
LIKE IT RE-STYLED IS THAT
YOU NEVER KNOW HOW
IT WILL END UP

HAVE YOU EVER STOPPED TO THINK JUST HOW
MUCH OF YOUR LIFE YOU SPEND
IN THE KITCHEN COOKING?

DON'T YOU AGREE THAT THE
CHRISTMAS HOLIDAYS GET LONGER
AND LONGER EVERY YEAR

DING DONG

AUNTIE! HOW LOVELY TO SEE YOU AGAIN AFTER ALL THIS TIME

2.5-2

THIS YEAR LET'S GIVE A PARTY

OH YES LET'S

SUPER

I'LL HAVE TO PAY BY CHEQUE

HATS

EVERYTHING FOR THE PARTY

WELL– IT WAS YOUR IDEA TO HAVE A PARTY

CAR PARK

© 1989 Barry Appleby   4-682

THIS YEAR LET'S NOT LEAVE EVERYTHING UNTIL THE LAST MINUTE

I'VE MADE A LIST OF WHAT'S TO BE DONE

GIFTS COOK

AND TO START WITH LET'S DECIDE WHAT YOU WANT FOR CHRISTMAS

THAT'S EASY

ADDRESS CARDS COOK PUD

PRESENTS COOK BUY GUEST LIST TREE VISIT DECORATE

A DIVORCE

© 1989 Barry Appleby

ADDRESS PRESENTS BUY COOK PARTY TREE VISIT

4-676

AND SO WE COME TO THE END OF YET ANOTHER
OF OUR ANNUALS — WE HOPE THAT YOU'VE
ENJOYED OUR FIRST EXPERIENCE WITH COLOURING
THE CARTOONS AS MUCH AS WE HAVE — IT'S BEEN
LOTS OF FUN

'BYE FOR NOW — SEE YOU IN THE MORNING
IN DAILY EXPRESS AND SUNDAY EXPRESS

WITH OUR BEST WISHES *George & Gaye*

©1990 *Barry Appleby*

Published by Express Newspapers plc, Blackfriars Road, London SE1 9UX.
Printed by Grosvenor Press (Portsmouth) Ltd. Reproduction by Graphic Origination, London.
Co-ordinated by Roeder Printer Services Ltd., London. Researched by Terry Greenwood